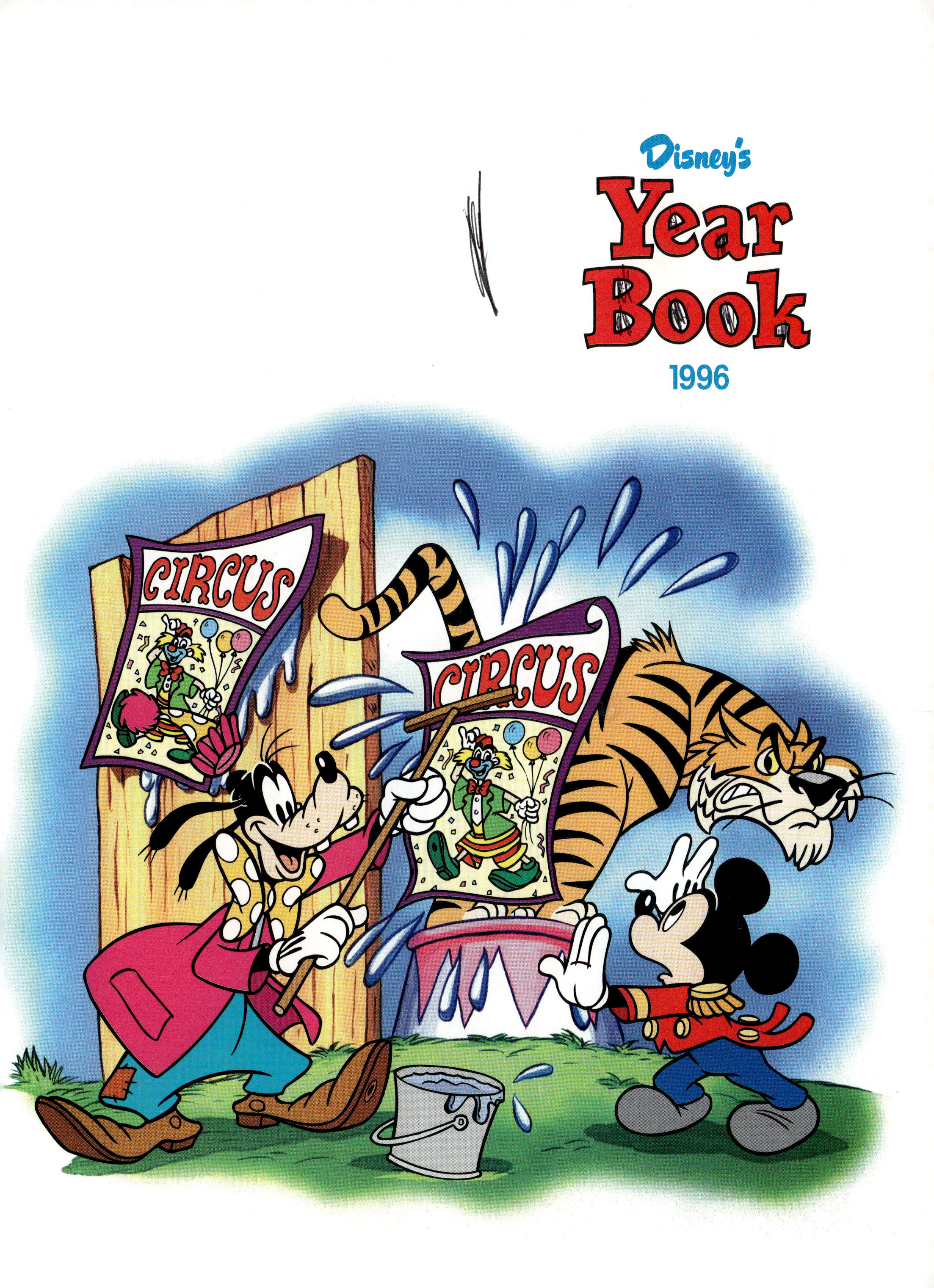
Disney's
Year
Book
1996
CIRCUS
CIRCUS

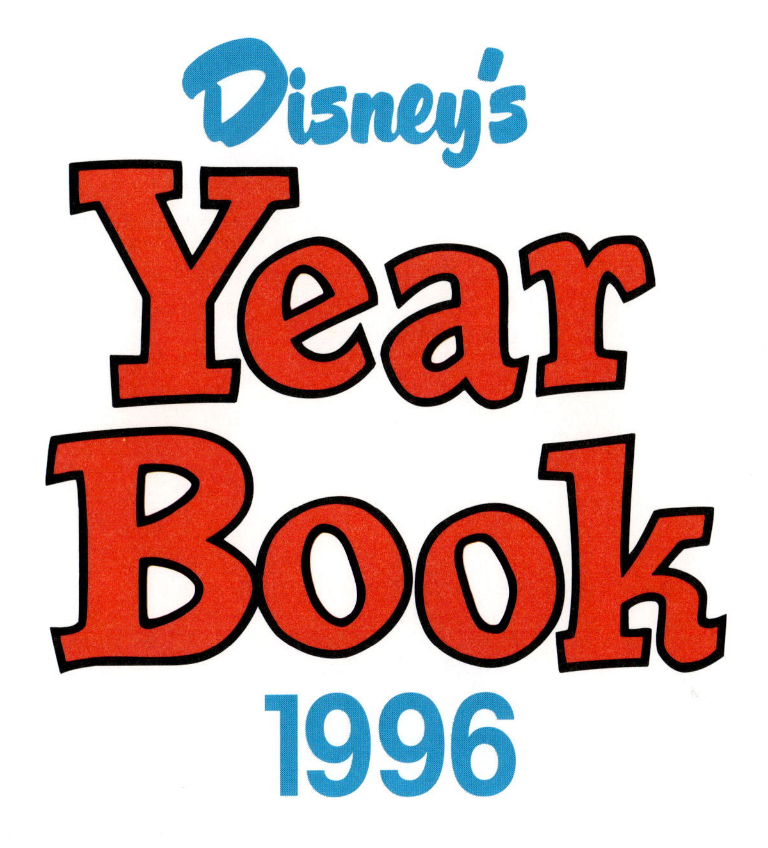

GROLIER ENTERPRISES INC.
Danbury, Connecticut

FERN L. MAMBERG — *Executive Editor*
ELIZABETH A. DEBELLA — *Art Director*
HARRIETT GREYSTONE — *Production Manager*

ISBN: 0-7172-8498-0
ISSN: 0273-1274

PRINTED IN THE UNITED STATES OF AMERICA

Illustration Credits and Acknowledgments

6—Lawrence Migdale; 7—Michel Delsol; 8—Jim Corwin/TSW; Otto Rogge/The Stock Market; © Gerry Ellis Nature Photography; 9—Frances M. Roberts; 10–11—Artist, Natasha Lessnik; 12—© Michael Dick/Animals Animals; 13—© Marty Snyderman/Animals Animals; © Dwight Kuhn; 14—© Thomas Eisner; 15—© Kim Taylor/Bruce Coleman Limited; 28—© Phil Matt; © *Palm Beach Post*; 29—© Lisa Loucks Christenson/Absolute Stock; 30—The Granger Collection; 31—Courtesy of Ringling Bros. and Barnum & Bailey Combined Shows; 32—David Woods/The Stock Market; 33—Courtesy Ringling Bros. and Barnum & Bailey Combined Shows; © Robert McElroy/Woodfin Camp & Associates; 34—Courtesy Ringling Bros. and Barnum and Bailey Combined Shows; 35—© Tom Hanson/Gamma Liaison; 48–49—Artist, Natasha Lessnik; 50—© Jean-Paul Ferrero/Auscape International; 51—Artist, Vince Caputo; 52—© Fritz Prenzel—Animals Animals; 53—© Hans & Judy Beste/Animals Animals; © Darren Leal/Auscape International; 54—© D. Parer & E. Parer Cook/ARDEA; © Tom McHugh/Photo Researchers, Inc.; 55—© Klaus Uhlenhut/Animals Animals; 56—Courtesy General Motors; Tribune Media Services; 57—U.S. Department of the Interior National Park Service, Edison National Historic Site; AP/Wide World; 70—© E.R. Degginger/Animals Animals; © Zig Leszczynski/Animals Animals; 71—© Maria Zorn/Animals Animals; © Bob & Clara Calhoun/Bruce Coleman Limited; 72—© Lee Snider; 73—© Sisee Brimberg/Woodfin Camp & Associates; 74—Photofest; 75—© Peter Saloutos/The Stock Market; © Russell R. Grundke/Unicorn Stock Photo; © Russell R. Grundke/Unicorn Stock Photo; 76–77—From *Make Cards!* © 1992 by F&W Publications. Used by permission of North Light Books, a division of F&W Publications, Inc.; 90–91—Dr. Gary S. Settles/Photo Researchers, Inc.; 92–95—Artist, Susan M. Waitt

Contents

A BIRTHDAY FOR EARTH DAY

What were you doing on April 22, 1995? Maybe you worked at a neighborhood recycling drive. Perhaps you and your classmates "adopted" an endangered species. Maybe you helped clean up a local park. However you spent the day, it was a special one. It was Earth Day—and it was the 25th anniversary of the first Earth Day.

Earth Day was started back in 1970 by people who were worried about the environment. Air and water were becoming more polluted. Natural resources were being wasted and used up. And wild animals and plants were dying out. To make everyone more aware of these problems, a special day was created. That first Earth Day was a huge success. Twenty million Americans took part in it. And it led to new laws to protect the environment.

But a few laws weren't enough. So in 1990 another Earth Day was held. This time, people all over the world took part. Earth Day has been held every year since then. And because of Earth Day, people are trying harder than ever to solve our environmental problems.

Enviro Cop on the Job

He's a huge walking hunk of junk. His head is a big plastic jug, and his body is covered with bottle caps, crushed cans, candy wrappers, and other bits of trash. Enviro Cop is funny-looking. But he's serious when he tells people to obey the four R's about trash: reduce (use less), reuse, recycle, and respond (take action).

New Yorker Ted Barnes created Enviro Cop, and his friend Ken Hunt wears the costume. With the help of two puppets—P.J. (a plastic jug) and Al (an aluminum can)—they put on shows at schools and shopping malls. Their message is simple: "If something can't be reduced, reused, or recycled, don't buy it."

People can help save our planet. Left: Solar collectors turn the sun's energy into electricity. This cuts down on the use of fossil fuels. Top: Recycling metal, paper, glass, and plastic saves precious natural resources. Right: Protecting animal habitats saves wildlife, such as these endangered cheetahs.

One problem is that we depend on fossil fuels (oil, coal, and natural gas) for most of our energy. But there is only a limited supply of these fuels, and people are concerned that they will be used up. They also worry about the pollution that is caused by the burning of fossil fuels. This is such a big problem that "Energy Efficiency" was made the theme of Earth Day 1995.

Energy efficiency means using less energy and not wasting it.

People need to build engines and factories that run better with less fuel. They need to use the energy from the sun and the wind to heat homes and produce electricity. And they need to design cars that run on electricity or fuels made from grains.

Trash is another problem. Most trash is buried in landfills, where it can pollute the air and water. And landfills are rapidly filling up. One way to solve this problem is to recycle used paper, metal, glass, and plastic. Then trash can be turned into new items—which also helps to save natural resources.

A third problem is that wild animals and plants are in danger of dying out all over the world. Most are endangered because people have destroyed their habitats—the places where they live. People have cut forests for timber. They have plowed prairies into farmland. And they have filled in marshes to build developments. Every plant and animal holds an important place in the web of life. And maintaining that web is what Earth Day is all about.

Kids were on the scene to help celebrate the 25th anniversary of Earth Day. They marched in parades, worked on clean-up drives, and planted trees.

PAPER POWER

Want to see some magic that helps the environment? Then just recycle your old newspapers and other paper goods. Presto! Your old paper is turned into new paper!

Abracadabra—
Paper Is Recycled
1. Used paper arrives at the paper mill.
2. The paper is shredded into tiny bits and then into fibers. Some new wood fibers are added.
3. The fibers go into a tank. They are mixed with water to make pulp.

How does this magic work? Most paper is made from wood that has been ground into fibers and mashed into pulp. To recycle it, you start by bringing newspapers, magazines, and other kinds of used paper to a recycling center. From there, the papers are sent to a paper mill. Then they are shredded and mashed and dumped into large tanks. Water is added to the tanks. The paper breaks down into fibers and is churned into pulp. Then the pulp is cleaned and sent through the papermaking process, just like pulp from new wood. It's mixed,

spread out to form a thin mat, pressed, dried, and finally smoothed into a finished sheet.

Some new wood fibers are always added to the recycled material. This gives the paper more strength. But recycling still saves many precious trees from being cut down.

Are You a Paper Waster?

The average person uses hundreds of pounds of paper a year. How much do you use? Want to get out from under that paper pile? Here are some tips:

- ***Save Paper.*** *Reuse grocery bags and giftwrap. Write on both sides of notebook paper. Use cloth napkins instead of paper ones.*
- ***Recycle.*** *Separate newspapers, magazines, cardboard, and other types of paper for recycling.*
- ***Use Recycled Paper.*** *Look for paper goods that have been made from recycled paper. Then you know that the fibers they are made from have already been used at least once.*

4. The pulp is washed and passed through screens to remove unwanted material.

5. The pulp is spread in a thin layer across a moving screen, called a wire. Water drains out, leaving a mat of fibers.

6. The mat goes through a series of rollers. These press out more water and dry and smooth the mat. The result is new paper, ready to be used again.

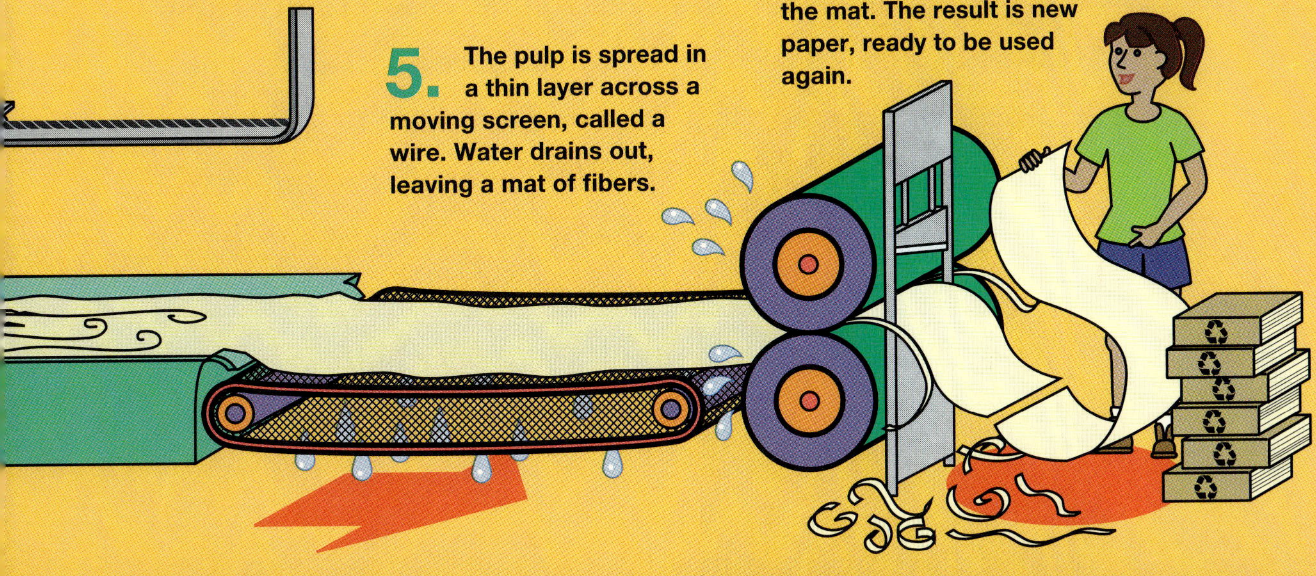

ANIMAL EYES

Why does the tarsier, the animal pictured at left, have such huge eyes? This Southeast Asian primate is active only at night, and its eyes help it to see in the dark. Like all animals, the tarsier has eyes that are designed for its way of life. In each case, an animal's eyes give it information it needs to survive.

The eye's first job is to sense light. Animals with very simple vision really can't do much more than that. The scallop, for example, has more than 200 eyes all around the edge of its soft body. However, it can "see" only light and some motion, but not images. When a scallop sees the moving shadow of an enemy, it can't tell what's actually out there. But it knows enough to quickly snap its shell closed!

Other animals have true eyes that, like yours, can see images—patterns of light that the animal's brain is able to identify. There are two basic kinds of true eyes: compound eyes and single-lens eyes.

Insects and crustaceans (such as lobsters and shrimps) have compound eyes. Each eye is made up of many tiny lenslets. Each lenslet takes in a separate image. But the animal blends the images to form a complete picture.

Animals with compound eyes see well only up close. A bee, for example, must fly right up to a flower to see it clearly. But then it sees the flower in almost microscopic detail. Animals

Left: The scallop has about 200 eyes around the edge of its body. It can sense light and motion, but not images. Right: The horsefly's compound eyes are made up of tiny lenslets. Each lenslet takes in a bit of a scene. The fly combines the bits to form a complete picture.

It's a world of a different color for most animals. For example, we see the bee on a yellow flower (left). But to the bee, the flower looks a glowing blue (right). This is because the flower has markings that are visible only in ultraviolet light (very short wavelengths of light). We can't see ultraviolet light—but the bee can.

with compound eyes can also see objects that are on all sides of them. If *you* want to see things to the side, you have to move your eyes or turn your head.

Mammals, birds, reptiles, amphibians, and fish have single-lens eyes. They see well at a distance. Single-lens eyes work like a camera. Light passes through a lens. The lens focuses the image on the retina at the back of the eye. The retina has special kinds of cells that detect light and color. These cells send signals to the brain. The brain interprets the signals and identifies the image.

The eyes of animals may be in different positions. Animals that are prey have eyes on the side of the head. This lets them keep watch over a wide area. But the eyes of predators are toward the front of the head. Your eyes are like this, too. This allows you to judge distances. You can do this because each eye takes in the scene ahead from a slightly different angle.

To see how it works, try this: Pick out a spot on a wall across the room. Close your right eye, and hold up your thumb to cover the spot. Now, without moving your thumb, close your left eye and open the right eye. Did your thumb "jump" to the left? When your brain blends the two views into one, it uses differences like this to judge how far away an object is.

Front and side aren't the only eye positions, though. The flounder has two eyes on one side of its body. Crabs and some other underwater animals have eyes on stalks. And the starfish has the oddest arrangement of all: its eyes are at the tips of its pointed arms.

Eyes at Night

Animals that are active at night often have huge eyes. This allows them to capture what little light there is and see in the darkness. An owl's eyes are so big, it can't move them in their sockets. The owl must turn its head to look around. But that's okay. Owls can twist their heads around to look almost straight back.

Have you ever seen the eyes of a dog or a cat "glow" in the dark? These animals have a special mirrorlike structure in their eyes. It captures and reflects the dim light of night. That helps the animal see—and also makes its eyes seem to glow.

LITTLE BRAVE HEART

"Nakoma, let's pick blackberries," Pocahontas suggested one hot summer day. "I found a patch full of ripe berries in a meadow up the river. We can go in my canoe."

"I love blackberries," Nakoma answered. "But should we go so far up the river without telling anyone?"

"Oh, we'll be back long before dark," Pocahontas answered as they climbed into her canoe with Meeko and Flit. Meeko sat in the front of the canoe and splashed his paws in the water. Flit flew beside the canoe as Nakoma and Pocahontas paddled.

At last they reached a small meadow beside the river. Pocahontas and Nakoma pulled the canoe onto a sandbar and walked into the meadow with Meeko and Flit close behind. The meadow was very pretty, with yellow and red flowers and deep, green grass. On the other side of the meadow, a steep rocky slope rose up to high stone bluffs. "My father said that one time it rained so hard the river rose till it covered this meadow all the way to the bluffs," Pocahontas told her friends as she led them to a big blackberry patch covered with shiny, juicy berries.

Meeko plumped right down and began stuffing berries into his mouth with both paws.

Little Flit wanted to help Pocahontas. He tried to lift a berry basket, but it was too heavy. Then he tried to pick the berries and bring them to Pocahontas. But the prickly branches stuck to his wings.

"Oh, Flit, thank you for trying to help, but you're just too tiny," Pocahontas said gently as she plucked the thorns from his wings.

Feeling very small and a little sad, Flit perched on a treetop alone. Below him, Pocahontas and Nakoma were singing as they picked berries. Meeko's tummy bulged as he stuffed berries into his mouth. Then, suddenly, a cold wind ruffled Flit's feathers. Flit looked at the sky and saw huge, black storm clouds on the horizon.

Flit flew down to Pocahontas. "I can't play now, Flit," she said. "I'm busy picking berries." He tugged a strand of her hair to make her look at the sky. But Pocahontas brushed him away. "Stop teasing me, Flit," she said sternly.

But Flit couldn't give up. He knew it was dangerous to be caught in a big storm far from the village. He tugged at Pocahontas's dress, trying to pull her toward the canoe. But Pocahontas still wouldn't pay any attention. "We're not leaving until we've filled our baskets, Flit," she said.

Just then, the wind blew the clouds over the sun. The sky grew dark. Thunder rumbled, and it began to rain.

As Meeko crawled beneath a berry basket to stay dry, Nakoma pointed toward the river. "Pocahontas, look!" she cried. "The river!"

Pocahontas looked through the pouring rain. Nakoma was right. The river was beginning to churn over the riverbank and fill the meadow. As they watched, the canoe was carried away.

"What should we do?" Nakoma asked. "The river is rising so fast it will soon flood the meadow."

"We must find shelter above the water!" Pocahontas replied. She looked around. But the rain was coming down so hard, she could barely see. “Flit, fly up and see if there is a place where we can all get out of the storm,” Pocahontas called.

Flit struggled up through the rain and saw a small cave halfway up the bluffs. He flew back to Pocahontas, then darted toward the cave. “Flit has found a place for us,” Pocahontas said. “Follow him!”

She picked up Meeko. Nakoma grabbed the full berry basket. They began to climb toward the cave. But the rocky ground was wet and slippery. With a cry, Nakoma slipped and fell, her foot twisted beneath her.

Pocahontas hurried to help her friend.

"Oh, no!" cried Nakoma. "I've hurt my ankle! I can't walk!"

"You can't lie here in the rain," said Pocahontas. "You must get up." She helped Nakoma stand. "Lean on me," Pocahontas said. Then she helped Nakoma limp toward the cave. Meeko and Flit went ahead of them. By the time they reached the cave, Nakoma was shaking from the cold, and her ankle was throbbing with pain.

"I must warm you, Nakoma," Pocahontas said. "But what can I use?" Flit noticed a pile of dried leaves and twigs the wind had blown inside the cave. He carried a leaf to Pocahontas. "Oh, Flit," she said, "you've found just what I need to

make a bed for Nakoma and a fire!" Pocahontas quickly fixed a soft bed of dry leaves for Nakoma. Then she made another pile of leaves and twigs. Next, she took a flintstone from the leather pouch at her waist.

"I will use the stone to strike a spark onto these leaves," she told Flit. "Fan the spark with your wings until it becomes a flame." Flit did as Pocahontas asked. In a few minutes, a cozy fire was warming the chilly cave.

"Now, if I only had some comfrey leaves to put on your ankle, they would stop the swelling," Pocahontas told Nakoma.

Flit remembered seeing some comfrey plants on the bluffs above the cave. He flew up, broke off two large leaves, and carried them to the cave.

"Thank you, Flit," Pocahontas said when she saw the leaves. She wrapped them around Nakoma's ankle and found a thong in her pouch to secure them.

"My ankle feels better already," Nakoma said.

Outside, the rain poured down. "Our families will be very worried," Pocahontas told Flit and Meeko, "and Nakoma should not stay in this cave too long, or she will become ill. But without my canoe, I can't go to the village for help. I don't know what to do."

Flit looked at the rain. He looked at the rising river. He knew he could fly across it to the village. Even though he was already wet and cold, Flit zipped out of the cave.

"Flit, come back!" Pocahontas called. But Flit would not turn back. The wind tossed him up and pushed him down. The rain soaked his wings and beat on his head. But Flit flew on. Thunder rumbled. Lightning flashed. The river roared and churned. But Flit kept on through the storm to the village.

Back at the cave, Pocahontas and her friends waited. Nakoma fell asleep on her leaf bed by the fire. Meeko ate all the berries. Pocahontas fed twigs to the fire and thought about Flit's journey. I hope he's safe, she thought. He's so small, and the storm is so big!

At last, the thunder and lightning faded. As Pocahontas looked out, the sun broke through the clouds, and a beautiful rainbow appeared over the flooded meadow.

Then Pocahontas saw the most beautiful sight of all. Up the river came a row of canoes. Her father, Chief Powhatan, was in the lead canoe. And in front of him, a tiny figure flashed and dazzled in the sun's rays. "It's Flit!" Pocahontas called to Meeko and Nakoma. "He's leading my father to us!"

The canoes paddled across the flooded meadow to the bluffs. Chief Powhatan and the warriors stepped from the canoes and followed Flit up to the cave.

The Chief and the other warriors carefully carried Nakoma to the canoes. Pocahontas, Meeko, and Flit followed closely behind. "Nakoma's ankle will mend well," Powhatan told his daughter. "You have taken good care of her."

"Thank you, Father," Pocahontas answered. "But Flit has taken the best care of us."

"It is true," Powhatan replied smiling. "He flew through the storm to lead us to you. Your tiny friend is very brave."

Flit perched on Pocahontas's shoulder. Pocahontas stroked him gently. "I will tell a story in the longhouse on feast days about how you saved us," she told him. "And in the story, I will give you a second name," Pocahontas continued. "You will always be Flit to me. But from now on, every time your story is told, you will be called Little Brave Heart."

POGMANIA

You can collect them. You can trade them. You can play with them. They are POGs, and they're hot, hot, HOT! And kids everywhere are caught up in the craze.

The story of the little cardboard disks called POG milk caps, or POGs, goes back more than 60 years. In those days, milk and juice were sold in glass bottles that were capped with cardboard disks. Dairies put ads on the caps, and kids collected and played with them. Then cardboard cartons and plastic bottles replaced the glass bottles. That should have been the end of milk caps—but it wasn't.

Around 1990, kids in Hawaii began playing a game that their parents had played with the earlier milk caps. They called the game POG because they used caps from a *p*assion-fruit, *o*range, and *g*uava juice drink made by a local dairy. Soon a POG frenzy swept Hawaii. When it spread to the rest of the United States and other countries, other companies also began to make milk caps.

Today's "milk caps" no longer cap any bottles. They are sold separately, often in packs like baseball cards. The caps are sold under various names, but most kids call them all POGs. And they are decorated with just about every design you can think of—action heroes, cartoon and storybook characters, sports stars, wild animals, cars!

Flipping Their Lids

It's fun to collect milk caps. But for many kids, it's playing the game that counts.

The basic POG game is very simple. Two players each put the same number of caps face up in one stack. The first player takes a heavier disk, called a slammer, and throws it down at the pile. Caps fly up, and the player gets to keep any that flip over. The rest are restacked for the second player's turn.

Some kids have gotten so upset at losing their milk caps that some schools have banned the caps. Now many kids play the game just for fun, not for keeps.

The GREATEST SHOW on EARTH

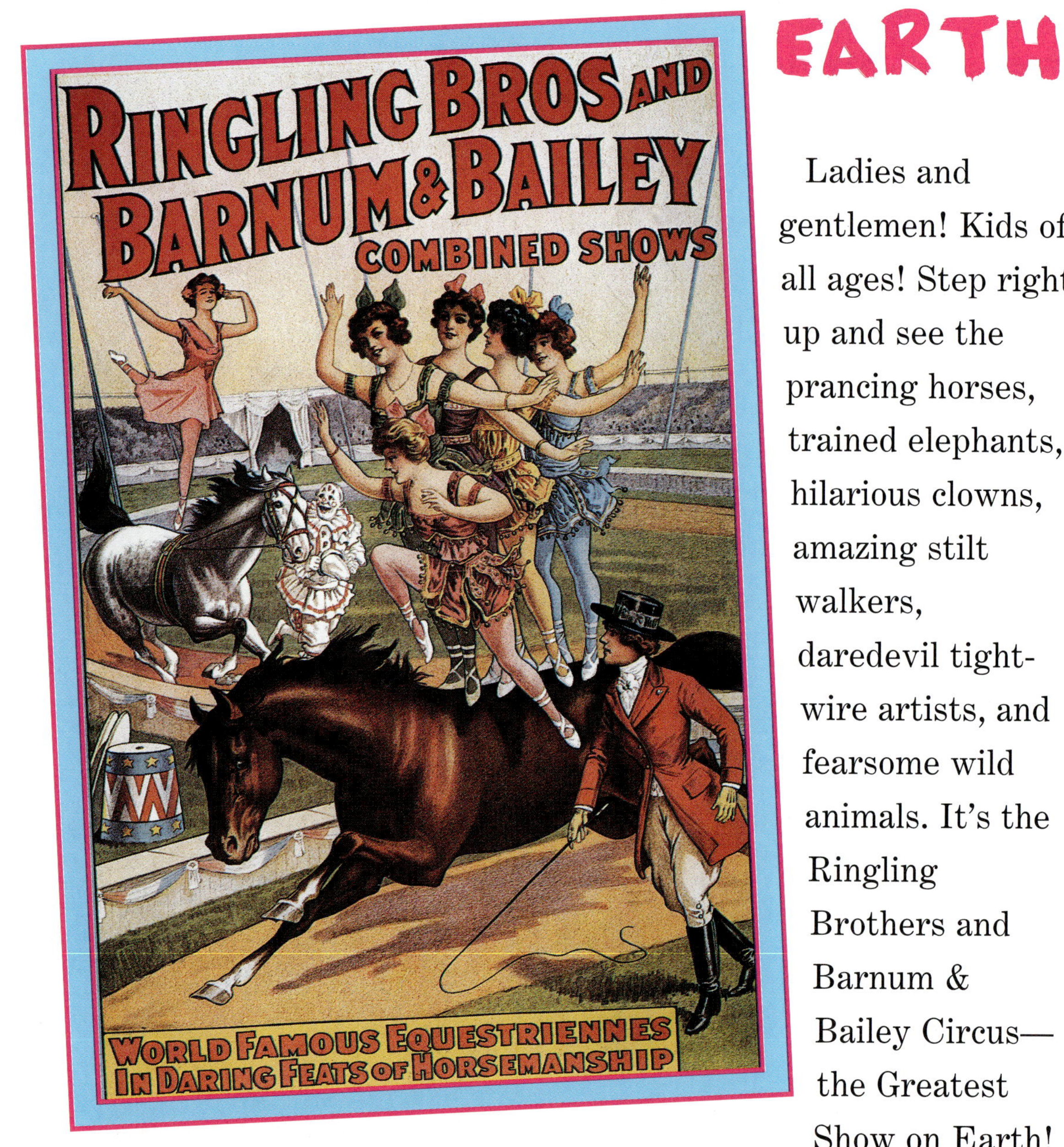

Ladies and gentlemen! Kids of all ages! Step right up and see the prancing horses, trained elephants, hilarious clowns, amazing stilt walkers, daredevil tight-wire artists, and fearsome wild animals. It's the Ringling Brothers and Barnum & Bailey Circus—the Greatest Show on Earth! Seen by 11 million people each year, this amazing three-ring show is the largest and most famous circus in the world. And in 1995, it celebrated 125 years of performances.

Ringling Brothers and Barnum & Bailey wasn't the first circus. Circuses have been around for more than 200 years. An Englishman named Philip Astley is known as "the father of the circus," and he began his shows in the 1760's. They were the first to include trick horseback riding, acrobats, rope walkers, and dancing dogs. His shows were so popular that others began to copy them, first in Britain and then in other countries. Circuses grew bigger and better.

In 1874, another British circus was the first to use trained elephants. American showman P. T. Barnum thought that was a great idea. So he bought an elephant named Jumbo for his circus in the United States. He claimed that Jumbo was the world's largest elephant, and people flocked to see the beast. Elephants still draw huge crowds to circuses.

Many people think that clowns are the best part of the circus. With their funny painted faces, bright costumes, and playful antics, clowns keep circusgoers in constant chuckles. Clowns also make the whole show run smoothly. They tumble into the arena between acts, and they often romp and frolic

while other acts are going on. Clowns perform in pantomime—they never speak. So they use lots of different comic routines and gags to amuse the audience. Clowns juggle. They do playful tricks. They perform crazy stunts like stuffing themselves into tiny cars. They race around on little unicycles, and they stroll along on towering stilts.

STILT WALKERS

High-wire walkers, trapeze artists, and other aerialists are exciting circus stars. Audiences gasp as they perform their daredevil feats high above the ground. All aerialists are good athletes and have many years of training. But most still use safety nets because their acts are so dangerous.

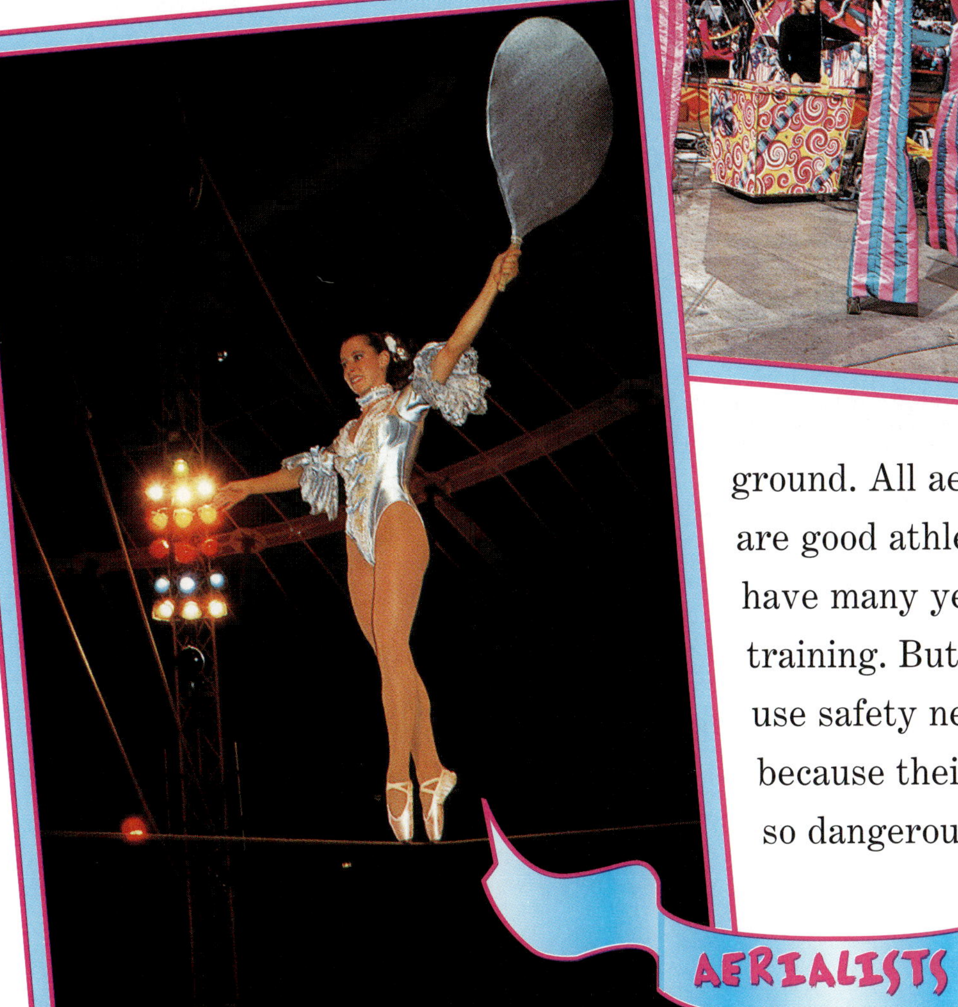

AERIALISTS

Elephants standing on their heads...sleek horses ridden by bareback riders...seals balancing balls on their noses...tigers leaping through rings of fire...monkeys doing acrobatic tricks...dogs dancing to ballet music. Animal acts of all kinds play a big part in the circus spectacle. People have always been amazed by a trainer's ability to teach an animal to perform. Especially popular are the wild-animal acts, in which jungle beasts and animal trainers come face to face in the ring. Hushed audiences watch as the trainer cracks a whip, and a snarling lion or tiger responds to every command. Some fearless trainers have even been known to ride a tiger, or to lie down in a cage full of leopards.

Cirque du Soleil: A Special Kind of Circus

The Cirque du Soleil ("Circus of the Sun") from Montreal, Canada, is a special kind of circus. There are no animals at all. And the clowns don't wear white face makeup or baggy pants. Instead, the performers do incredible acrobatic feats to the music of a rock band. They wear dazzling costumes. They use spectacular lighting effects and high-tech stage settings. The Cirque du Soleil is a mix of circus and drama. It has toured North America, Europe, and Japan—and audiences everywhere love it. This highly unusual show is one of the most thrilling circuses ever.

The circus is a remarkable supershow that combines magic and mystery and excitement. The next time you hear that "the circus is coming to town," make sure you and your family get tickets and bags of popcorn and share in the fun!

THE ONE THAT GOT AWAY

"Wak!" Donald cried as he tumbled out of the hammock.

"Stop! You no-good cattle rustlers!" yelled Huey, galloping by on a stick hobbyhorse.

"Ha! Ha!" laughed Dewey, leaping over Donald.

"Ha! Ha!" laughed Louie, right behind his brother. "Sheriff Huey can't catch us!" he shouted.

"Yeow!" sputtered Donald. The ends of Dewey's and Louie's hobbyhorses jabbed and poked him.

His nephews stopped playing. "You okay, Unca Donald?" Dewey asked.

"Hmmmf," snorted Donald. "This is my weekend off. My two days to do whatever I please. And it would please me to have a little peace and quiet!"

"Sorry, Unca Donald!" Louie called, and he and his brothers ran off.

Donald tried to untangle the hammock but only succeeded in tying the hammock into knots. "And you can fix my hammock!" he called after the boys.

Well, Donald didn't want to take a nap now, anyway. Maybe he'd work on his ship model of *Miss-Daisy*-in-a-bottle.

Donald went into his den and took down the ship-in-a-bottle that he'd been building for months. He carefully unwrapped the parts that still needed to be glued onto the ship and picked up a delicate mast. Donald slowly slipped his hand into the bottle. He almost had the mast in position when the floor suddenly began to shake.

"And a 5-6-7-8..." he heard Daisy shout above the pounding music.

"Oh, no!" moaned Donald when the mast snapped in half. He'd forgotten that Daisy's All-Girl Tap and Drum Corps were practicing in the playroom that morning.

“That regional All-Girl Tap and Drum Corps performance is at the old theater tonight, and the floor is being polished now,” Donald grumbled. “If the new theater were done, then Daisy and her team would be practicing there! But, instead, here they are tapping and drumming and shaking *my* house!”

There was no way Donald could work on *Miss Daisy* while Daisy and her friends were dancing. Fuming, Donald packed a sandwich, grabbed his fishing rod, and headed out the door.

"Ah, peace and quiet at last!" he sighed after rowing to his favorite fishing spot. With his line baited and his rod in one hand, Donald unwrapped his sandwich and began to eat. But before he could take a single bite, waves rocked the boat and threw Donald against the side.

Vrooom! Vrooom! roared a high-speed motorboat. "Hi ya, Donald!" hollered Goofy on water skis.

"Hmmmf," snorted Donald. "I didn't know Goofy could water ski. Uh-oh!" Goofy was coming closer and closer, and faster and faster, right toward Donald's little rowboat. Donald held onto the sides of the boat. The wake from the motorboat tossed the little rowboat back and forth as if it were a toy. Donald thought, "Don't wave, Goofy! Don't let go of the..."

"Hi ya, Donald!" Goofy waved.

"Oh, no!" cried Donald.

"Gawrsh!" Goofy exclaimed as his skis flipped up, throwing him head over skis over Donald.

"Duck!" Goofy yelled. And duck Donald did—just in the nick of time.

"Wak!" wailed a soggy Donald Duck, dripping from head to foot.

"Sorry, Donald! See ya later!" Goofy hollered, skiing away.

Poor Donald! He and his sandwich were soaked. Grumbling, Donald started to reel in his line. He felt a slight tug. "What's this? Maybe my day won't be a total loss, after all," Donald chuckled. He carefully reeled in his prize and lifted the line out of the water.

It was a fish! A shimmering, golden fish! Donald had never seen anything like it. He gently took the hook out and put the fish in a pail of water.

The fish looked at Donald and said, "Release me, fisherman, for I am magic and can make your wishes come true."

Donald shook his head in disbelief, "Ha! A magic fish? I don't believe it," he scoffed. "Prove it!" He showed his waterlogged lunch to the fish. "Unsoak my soggy sandwich!"

"I can do better than that," said

the fish. She shivered and shook her golden scales. In a magical flash an enormous picnic basket filled with Donald's favorite foods appeared.

"Wow! I'm convinced!" Donald exclaimed, and he put the fish back in the lake. But before she swam away, the magic fish said, "What you wish for, I will grant. You have two more wishes, fisherman. Use them wisely and well."

"Oh, boy!" Donald cried, diving into the picnic basket. As he ate, he thought about all the things he might wish for. "I could wish for *Miss-Daisy*-in-a-bottle to be finished. I could wish for the lawn mower to mow by itself!" Donald shook his head. "Think big," he told himself. "That's what Uncle Scrooge does! Uncle Scrooge! Of course!" Then Donald knew just what he'd wish for. "I'll find my piggy bank, hold it in my hands, and wish for as much money as Uncle Scrooge has!"

Donald quickly rowed back to the dock, tied up the boat, and ran all the way home. Racing up the steps, he slipped on a skate and once again fell into his nephews' Wild West game.

"Oomph!" exclaimed Donald as Dewey tripped and landed on top of his uncle.

Dewey gave his uncle a hand getting up and said, "Sorry, Unca Donald. I sure wish we could be riding real horses."

"Well," replied Donald, "I wish you could, too, but..." There was a second magical flash, and Huey, Dewey, and Louie suddenly found themselves on horseback, riding off to a campfire cookout.

"Wow! Thanks, Unca Donald! You're the best!" the nephews cried.

"Oh, no," groaned Donald. "My wish!"

Donald waved to the boys as they rode off, but muttered under his breath, "Well, this last wish is for *me*!"

Donald began looking for his piggy bank and found a note from Daisy. It said:

> *Donald Dear, thank you for letting us practice in the playroom. We went to the old theater for a final dress rehearsal before tonight. See you then! Love, Daisy.*

Just as Donald finished reading the note, he heard *Waaa! Waaa! Waaa!* the wailing of the fire alarm, calling all volunteer fire-fighters to help put out a fire. From the window Donald could see what was on fire. It was the old theater—the same old theater where Daisy and the All-Girl Tap and Drum Corps were performing that evening! The same old theater where

Daisy and her team had gone for a dress rehearsal! Donald grabbed his firefighter's gear and dashed out of the house.

The firefighters soon had the blaze under control, but the old theater was beyond saving. The new theater was only half done. Daisy ran to Donald, sobbing. He put his arm around her. "Oh, Donald," she wept, "how I wish the new theater were ready!"

"I do, too," said Donald in sympathy. In a third magical flash, the new theater was built. Daisy's tears dried instantly.

Daisy hugged Donald and said, "Now we can have our show tonight! And we can have our dress rehearsal right on schedule!" She and her All-Girl Tap and Drum Corps rushed into the new theater.

Donald stomped off. "Three wishes! Three wasted wishes!" At home, Donald grabbed a newspaper and went to lie down in the hammock his nephews had thoughtfully untangled for him. Brooding, Donald said, "All I wanted was a little peace and quiet. And what happens? Magic fish! Horses for my nephews! A new theater for Daisy! What did *I* get? Lunch!" Donald looked around. It was rather quiet and somewhat peaceful, too. "Hmmmf! Looks like I got my peace and quiet," he was forced to admit.

Donald sighed, lay back in his hammock, and closed his eyes.

CALCULATOR TALK

Did you know that your pocket calculator can do more than arithmetic? It can talk to you! Well, almost. Would you like to get acquainted? Multiply .3867 by 2. To do this, press down on the decimal point (.), then the digits 3, 8, 6, and 7. Press the multiply (×) button. Then enter the number 2. Press the equals (=) button. Now turn the calculator upside down. See how friendly your calculator can be!

Here's some more calculator talk:

1. Before you can eat an _ _ _, you must break the shell. ($1986 \div 2 =$)

2. If you are very messy, you may be called a _ _ _ _. ($2 \times 4000 + 75 =$)

3. You can see lots of animals at the _ _ _. ($0.06 \div 3 =$)

4. A _ _ _ produces honey. ($151 \times 2 + 36 =$)

5. When Santa Claus comes down the chimney, he says _ _ _ _ _ _ (1.21212 ÷ 3=)

6. A scared snake might rise up and _ _ _ _ at you. (11 × 500 + 14 =)

7. You might get an upset stomach if you _ _ _ _ _ _ your food. (47250 × 8 + 809=)

8. Jessica is taking lessons to learn to play the _ _ _ _ . (4555 − 1475=)

9. A _ _ _ _ _ is helpful to a student studying geography. (9 × 4231 =)

10. People who are sad might cry _ _ _ _ _ _. (0.32064 ÷ 8 =)

GIGGLE

379919

You may have figured out which numbers form which letters:

I	Z	E	H	S	L	B	G	O
1	2	3	4	5	7	8	9	0

Use these letters to come up with more calculator words. Then try to make your own sentence-puzzles with them.

This furry little critter, called a quokka, is a small kangaroo. It's just one of the many unusual animals that live in Australia.

Australia's Unusual Animals

What's a quokka? A cuscus? A bandicoot? They may sound like imaginary creatures from some weird space movie. In fact, they are some of the special animals found only in Australia and a few nearby islands—and nowhere else in the world.

Why does Australia have so many special animals? Millions of years ago, the world didn't look the way it looks now. All the land on Earth formed one supercontinent. Gradually it broke apart, and the continents that we know today slowly drifted to their present positions. Australia ended up far away from the other continents. As a result, its animals were cut off from animals in other places, and so they developed differently.

Many of Australia's unusual animals are marsupials—mammals with pouches outside their bodies, in which their babies develop. Kangaroos are the country's most famous—and largest—marsupials. The kangaroos that you are probably most familiar with are the big red kangaroo and the gray kangaroo. These animals can be taller and heavier than a human adult, and they hop across the plains at 40 miles an hour. However, many kangaroos are much smaller. The little quokka, for example, is a kangaroo about the size of a large dog. But quokkas, like their much bigger cousins, have long hind legs and feet that allow them to hop about very quickly.

WHAT'S A MARSUPIAL?

Marsupials are mammals. Like other mammals, they have fur. Their young are born live. And they are nourished by their mother's milk.

Most mammal babies develop inside the mother's body. They get nourishment there. But a marsupial baby spends very little time inside its mother's body. When it is born, it's only about an inch long, and it has a lot more growing to do. So it crawls to one of its mother's nipples, which is usually in a pouch on the mother's belly. There the baby drinks its mother's milk and continues to develop.

PROTECTING THE CUDDLY KOALA

Many Australian marsupials are in danger of dying out, or becoming extinct. One of them, the koala, isn't on the endangered species list. But some people are afraid it could be.

Koalas are picky eaters—they eat only the leaves of certain eucalyptus trees. As trees are cut down where koalas live, they lose their food supply.

More eucalyptus trees are being planted in Australia to make sure that koalas will have food in the future. Australians don't want to lose these precious animals that look like living teddy bears.

Another of Australia's well-known marsupials is the koala. With its plump, furry, pear-shaped body, sleepy eyes, and big ears, the koala is one of the cutest animals in the world. Koalas are terrific climbers and spend most of their lives in trees. Weighing up to 30 pounds, they are one of the world's largest tree-dwelling mammals.

Australian possums are a big family of animals. They are all plant-eating marsupials that are active at night. The smallest is the honey possum, which is just a few inches long. This little possum has been nicknamed the marsupial hummingbird because it feeds on flower nectar, just like a hummingbird does.

With its two-foot-long body and two-foot-long tail, the cuscus is the largest possum. A

The spotted cuscus moves v-e-r-y s-l-o-w-l-y around its treetop home.

slow-moving tree-dweller, it looks like a cross between a monkey and a sloth. It has large bulging eyes, tiny ears, and thick fur.

Australia's bandicoot, with its long, pointy nose, has sometimes been mistaken for a rat. But it, too, is a marsupial. Bandicoots are shy animals that live on the ground and hunt at night. Like kangaroos, they can stand on their hind legs. However, they use all four legs to hop around. Most bandicoots have bristly fur. One kind, the rabbit bandicoot, has a silky coat and long rabbitlike ears.

The rabbit bandicoot's long, silky ears alert it to danger.

Australia is also home to many unusual animals that aren't marsupials. Two of the oddest are the platypus and the echidna. With its velvety fur coat, webbed feet, and a broad bill like a duck's, the platypus is a strange-looking creature. The echidna, also called the spiny anteater, has sharp spines mixed in among its fur, making it resemble a porcupine. It uses its long, tubelike snout and sticky tongue to get some tasty treats—ants and termites. The platypus and the echidna

The echidna (left) and the platypus (below) are the only mammals in the world that lay eggs.

don't look alike, yet they are cousins. Both are mammals—they have fur and their young are nourished by the mother's milk. But they are the only mammals in the world that lay eggs!

One of Australia's most unusual reptiles is the frilled lizard. This animal can grow to be three feet long, and it is named for a special feature that it has. When the frilled lizard is cornered, it opens its mouth and lets out a loud whistling hiss. Then it unfurls a huge fanlike collar around its neck. This collar makes the lizard's head look much larger than it really is, which scares off most enemies. But there really isn't much to be scared of. The frilled lizard is all bluff—it would rather flee than fight.

The animals described on these pages are just a few of the unique creatures found in Australia, a very special continent.

The frilled lizard's huge collar makes the animal look more fierce than it really is.

The new two-seat Impact shown above may not look very different from other cars on the road. But it won't work unless its battery is plugged in and recharged! The Impact is one of several electric cars that are now being developed.

ELECTRIC CAR
$15,000.
GM
THAT'S FIVE THOUSAND FOR THE CAR AND TEN THOUSAND FOR THE EXTENSION CORD...

PLUG IT IN, WATCH IT GO

The race is on: Which carmaker will build the best electric automobiles? These are cars that run on batteries that must be recharged. Electric vehicles, also called EV's, aren't a new idea. In the early days of the automobile, electric motors were used to power many cars. But they lost out to gasoline-powered cars, which could go farther and faster. Today, EV's are once again being built. The reason is pollution. The exhaust from gasoline-powered cars is full of harmful chemicals. EV's produce no fumes at all. And the motors are much quieter.

Some EV's now being developed can go as fast as 100 miles an hour. But they run on big, heavy batteries that must be recharged every 75 to 100 miles. This is done by plugging them into regular electric current—for up to eight hours. Most gasoline-powered cars can go three times as far on a tank of fuel. And it takes just minutes to refill the tank. So researchers are working hard to make better EV batteries.

EV's of the future may make the fumes and noise of gasoline-burning cars a thing of the past.

Electric Vehicles—Past and Present

Inventor Thomas Alva Edison (above left) sits in a 1911 electric vehicle. "Electricity is the thing," he said. "There is...no dangerous and evil-smelling gasoline." This early EV could go 80 miles between charges. Today's EV's don't do much better—and some do worse: France's new electric TULIP (below) may be fun to drive, but it can go only 43 miles before recharging.

THE OUTBACK ADVENTURE

"I'm too pooped to walk another inch," Pumbaa told Timon as they hiked through the Australian outback.

"Me, too," Timon agreed. He sat down on a large, oval-shaped greenish rock. "Australians call hiking a walkabout, and now I know why. You walk about as far as you can before your feet fall off!"

Timon began to rub his tired, hot feet. Suddenly, the stone he was sitting on jerked so hard, Timon fell off. "Pumbaa, this rock just rolled—by itself!" Timon yelped, staring at the stone. As he watched, huge cracks appeared. A sharp yellow beak poked out, followed by a tiny head and a long, scrawny neck. In a few minutes a baby emu emerged.

"Timon, you were sitting on an egg! You hatched an emu!" Pumbaa laughed. The little chick saw Timon and squeaked happily. It stumbled over and rubbed against him. "Look, Timon," Pumbaa chuckled. "The little guy thinks you're his mama."

"Shoo! Go away! Move it! I'm not your mother!" Timon shouted. He backed away, but the baby emu followed him. It opened and shut its beak, squeaking loudly.

"He's hungry," Pumbaa said. "Let's find him some bugs to eat."

Soon the little emu was gulping down grubs and squawking for more. Timon scooped up a handful of beetles. The baby bird

swallowed them and squeaked again. Timon tossed ants into the little bird's mouth like popcorn. But still, the little bird squawked.

"Whoever said eating like a bird meant not eating much sure didn't know what he was talking about," Timon gasped as he and Pumbaa ran back and forth with bugs for the baby bird. "I don't think we can keep this up for long."

"Maybe we should try to find his real mom," Pumbaa said.

So the two friends set off with the little bird to look for his mother. Soon they came to a eucalyptus grove. "Birds like trees," Pumbaa said. "Maybe the mama emu is here."

The trio hurried into the grove of trees and looked around. The little bird squawked loudly for more to eat. "Be quiet!" a voice yelled suddenly from high in the trees. Timon and

Pumbaa looked up and saw a koala yawning above them. The koala rubbed its eyes. "Tell that noisy little squawker to be quiet," the koala snapped. "He woke me up."

"We're sorry," Timon said. "We're just looking for this little guy's mama. Have you seen her?"

"No," the koala answered. "I'm napping. Or at least I *was* napping. Now scram, so I can get some rest." The koala began throwing sticks and leaves at Timon, Pumbaa, and the little emu. A large stick fell near Timon.

"Wow! Great walking stick," he said. He picked it up and ran out of the grove as more sticks and leaves rained down.

"That koala wasn't much help," Pumbaa said as he walked on.

"Well, koalas sleep during the day, you know," Timon explained. "And Mr. Loud Beak did wake him up, after all."

All day they trudged, looking everywhere for a flock of emus. They climbed up rolling hills and clambered down rocky ridges. They walked around bushes and crawled through tall grass. But they didn't see a flock of emus anywhere.

At last they came to a wide, brown river. "Water!" Timon shouted. "Just what my feet need. My toes feel like french fries." He waded into the river's shallow edge.

"But how are we going to get across, Timon?" Pumbaa asked. "We can't swim."

Suddenly an enormous crocodile rose from the water. With a shriek, Timon jumped back to the bank. The crocodile grinned at

him. "Don't be afraid," he said, smiling slyly. "I heard you wondering how to cross the river. I'll carry you on my back."

"Yeah, and then you'll gobble us up," Timon answered.

"No I won't." The crocodile smiled wider. "I'm not hungry—yet. Just climb on. There's room inside—er, I mean on board—for you all."

But Timon was still suspicious. "Watch every move this guy makes," Timon whispered to Pumbaa. "I don't trust him."

"Oh, Timon. He's just trying to help," Pumbaa argued.

"Besides, he has such a nice, big smile. He *must* be friendly."

So Timon, Pumbaa, and the little bird climbed onto the crocodile's back and sat down, and the crocodile swam across the river.

But just as they were about to

reach the opposite bank, the crocodile twisted his head around and snapped at them. “Fooled you,” he grinned.

“Grab the bird and jump to the bank,” Timon shouted. “I’ll take care of Mr. Scale Breath.”

As Pumbaa and the little emu leaped ashore, Timon jammed his walking stick between the crocodile’s jaws and wedged them open. Then he jumped to the bank, too.

Timon, Pumbaa, and the little bird ran as fast as they could. When the river was far behind them, they stopped to rest. They were very hot and tired.

“What do we do now, Timon?” Pumbaa asked. “We’ve looked everywhere. But we still haven’t found this baby’s mother.”

As Timon and Pumbaa thought about their predicament, a mama kangaroo hopped by. She was peering around bushes and behind rocks. “Joey! Oh, Joey, where are you?” the kangaroo called.

“Look, Timon,” Pumbaa said. “A mama kangaroo.”

“Pumbaa, we’re looking for a mama emu, not a mama kangaroo,” Timon answered.

“But Timon—kangaroos have pockets,” Pumbaa explained. “Maybe the little bird could climb inside and...”

Timon shook his head. “Pumbaa, that idea is so dumb it’s...”

Then he got the idea himself. Timon snapped his fingers. “Pumbaa, I have an idea!” he shouted. “Maybe the kangaroo would give the baby a ride to its mother. She can hop much farther and faster than we can walk.”

“That’s what I thought,” Pumbaa answered. But Timon was already running over to speak with the kangaroo.

The sun was in the kangaroo’s eyes, and she couldn’t see very well. When she saw Timon, she thought he was her little kangaroo. “Oh, Joey, you naughty little kangaroo!” she cried. “I’ve been looking everywhere for you!”

“I’m not Joey, I’m Timon and—” Before Timon could say another word, the mama kangaroo popped him into her pouch.

“We’re going back to the rest of the kangaroos right now,” she said. Off she bounded in great leaps.

“Puuuuumbaa!” Timon shrieked as he bounced up. “Ooof!” He groaned as he jounced down. “Saaaave! Ugh! Meeee! Ooof!”

Pumbaa slung the little emu onto his back and dashed after Timon and the kangaroo. They arrived just as Timon crawled from the mama kangaroo’s pouch and flopped to the ground. A little kangaroo ran up. “Who’s this, Mama?” he asked, looking at Timon. “Oh, my goodness!” the mama kangaroo exclaimed. “I thought it was you, Joey. I thought I was bringing you back, but you were already here.”

"I tried to tell you," Timon spluttered. "But it's very hard to talk when you're being bounced around like a beach ball."

"I'm so sorry," the mama kangaroo said. "Is there anything I can do to help you now? Would you like a ride back?"

"Oh, no, thank you. I'll just walk," Timon answered quickly.

"But Timon—maybe there *is* something she could do," Pumbaa spoke up. He put the baby emu in front of the mama kangaroo. "We've been trying all day to help this little bird find his mama," he told the kangaroo. "You travel so fast and so far, perhaps you could take him to his flock."

"Why, I saw a flock of emus not far from here," the mama kangaroo answered. "I'll take the little bird to them. His mama will be there, I'm sure."

"Thank you," Timon said as the kangaroo lifted the little bird into her pouch. Joey climbed in, too.

"Well, good-bye, little guy." Timon and Pumbaa patted the baby emu on the head. It peeped happily and waved a stubby wing at them as it bounced away in the mama kangaroo's pouch.

Timon and Pumbaa watched until the kangaroo was out of sight. Then they grinned at each other. "Say, Timon," Pumbaa said, "this was quite a day for you. You've been a bird's mama, and a kangaroo's kid. What are you going to be next? A monkey's uncle?"

*The lovely **blue morpho butterfly** glimmers because its wings are covered by countless tiny scales. Each scale has layers that reflect light. However, only male morphos have beautiful coloring. The females are brown.*

*The **cardinal tetra** is a very flashy fish. Over its brilliant scarlet belly is an iridescent blue-green band. Scales that catch and bend the light give the band its glimmer. Cardinal tetras are popular freshwater aquarium fish.*

GLITTER CRITTERS

Some birds, fish, and insects glitter and gleam with glowing colors. Their sparkling beauty comes from a remarkable natural wonder called iridescence. Iridescent colors are bright and metallic. And the colors shift and change as you look at them.

The brilliant ***tiger beetle*** *glows with metallic tones—green, gold, bronze, and blue. Its hard outer covering is made up of many layers. This produces its iridescent sheen. Some types have stripes and bars, like the tigers for which they are named.*

As the tiny male ***Anna's hummingbird*** *zooms from flower to flower to dine on nectar, it glitters like a flying jewel. Its pinkish-red head and green back glow with iridescence because its feathers have a thin coating that bends and reflects light.*

Certain rocks, gems, and even soap bubbles are also iridescent. They glitter because their surfaces have more than one layer. The different layers reflect different colors.

Iridescent animals produce their gleaming colors in the same way—they have layered body surfaces. Each surface catches the light and bounces it back, creating a rainbow of shimmering shades. The animals look just like living jewels.

Great Gargoyles

You're walking along a city street. You look up. Perched high above on a building are horrible creatures with big open mouths—and they are staring down at you! Don't be afraid. They aren't alive. They're made of stone, and they're known as gargoyles.

Gargoyles can look like fantastic animals...or goblins... or demons...or dragons...or weird people. Many are scary. But some are comical. Where did these peculiar stone carvings come from, and what are they used for?

A group of gruesome gargoyles decorates a French cathedral that was built hundreds of years ago during the Middle Ages.

Gargoyles were first used on buildings in Europe more than 800 years ago, during a period of time called the Middle Ages. They were placed on many of the ornate Gothic cathedrals that were then being built. The carvings stuck out from the sides of the cathedral, and they had a very important use—they were rainspouts. Gargoyles were connected to the roof gutters. Rainwater ran from the building roof, along the gutters, through the hollow gargoyles, and out their mouths. This prevented rainwater from flowing down the stone walls of the building and damaging them.

This gargoyle on the Washington National Cathedral serves as a rainspout—the true purpose of Gothic gargoyles.

The name "gargoyle" gives a clue to its use as a rainspout: It comes from an Old French word that means "throat." The word "gargle" comes from the same word. There are also gargoyle-like carvings that aren't rainspouts. These are called grotesques, and they are used on buildings mainly for decoration.

People wonder why the Gothic gargoyles were made to look so monstrous. Perhaps the frightening shapes were meant to keep evil spirits away from the cathedral, and to remind people to be good. Or perhaps the stone carvers were simply letting their imaginations run wild in dreaming up the odd shapes.

Gargoyles first appeared in America in the 1800's, not only on churches but also on public buildings and homes. There aren't many buildings now being designed in the Gothic style. But one of the most famous is the Washington National Cathedral, in Washington, D.C. Completed in 1990, after 83 years of work, it has more than a hundred gargoyles and grotesques on the outside! The stone carvers who worked on this cathedral added a touch of playfulness to their creations. Among the carvings are a caveman carrying a club, a long-haired hippie, and a person eating a turkey drumstick.

Gargoyles to the Rescue

Evildoers are everywhere. Who will save us? Batman? Superman? Nope! The Gargoyles are here! They are the heroes of Disney's popular TV cartoon series, "Gargoyles." The stone statues, which once decorated a castle in Scotland, have now been transported to a New York City skyscraper. By day they sit atop the building—but at night they take wing to help the police battle the forces of evil.

Demons, unicorns, and bears are some of the unusual figures used for gargoyles and grotesques.

Today, gargoyles are making a comeback—but not on buildings. Their stone shapes pop up in gardens and alongside swimming pools. They appear in children's books. They're on TV in an animated cartoon series. There are also gargoyle pencil holders, bookends, paperweights, cuddly stuffed toys...even canned pasta in the shape of gargoyles.

Whatever strange forms gargoyles may take, it seems that they will always be both fantastic and fascinating.

POP-UP GREETINGS

Want to celebrate a birthday...cheer up a friend...just say "hello"? Then make your own cards that POP to life!

These pop-up cards lie flat when they are closed—and then stand up to form 3-D images when opened.

1. To make the card, cut out a sturdy piece of paper. Fold it in half.

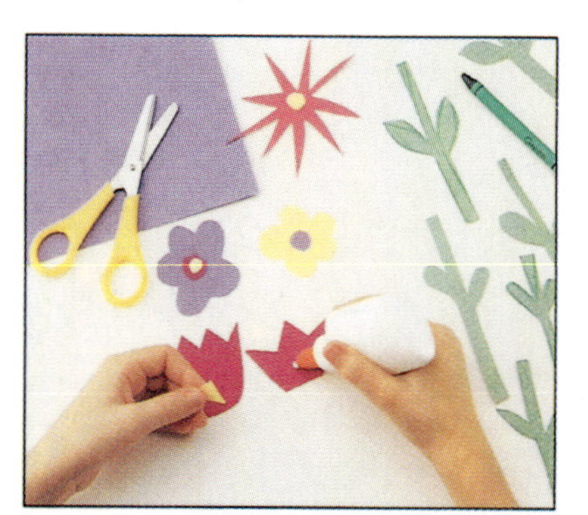

2. Cut out flowers and stems from colorful construction paper.

3. Make the vase by cutting out a rectangular piece of paper. Fold it in half. Fold each edge back to make two flaps.

The card on the opposite page pops up with a vase filled with colorful flowers. The instructions below tell how to make it.

Another idea for a pop-up card is the park scene shown at right. You will need construction paper, white paper, crayons, and white glue.

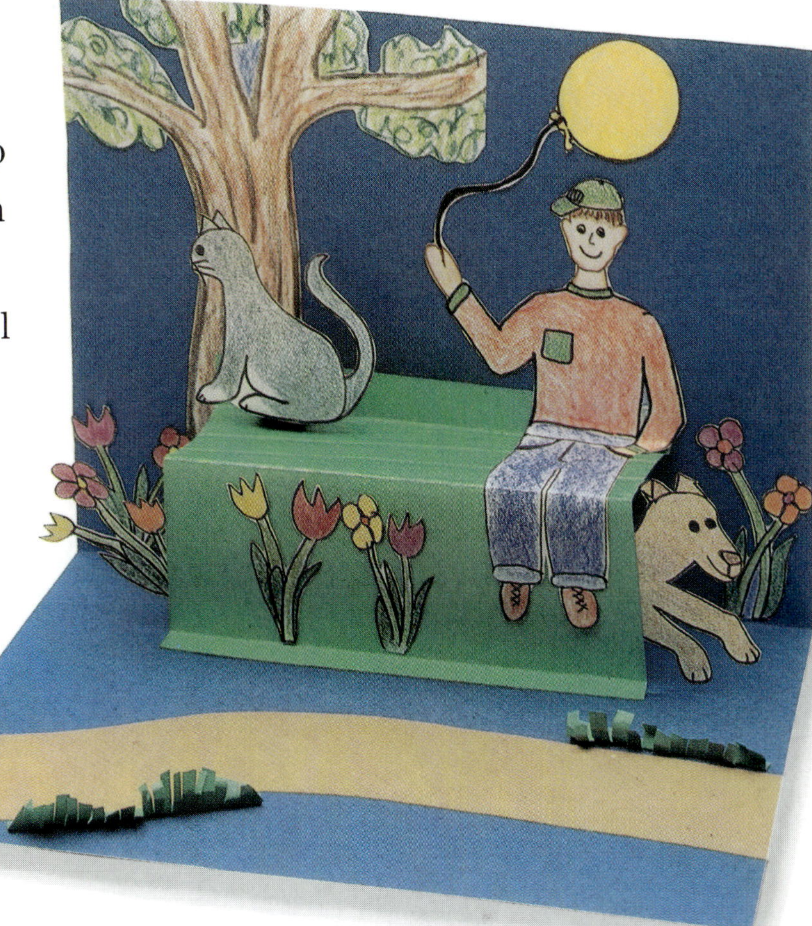

4. Place the V-shaped fold over the card's center fold, so that the V stands up a little.

5. Glue down the flaps of the vase to the card. Let it dry.

6. Glue some of the flowers to the inside of the vase, and some to the card. Decorate card and vase.

THE SURPRISE PARTY

"Wow, will you look at all those flashing pictures!" the Gargoyle named Brooklyn called to his friends Lexington and Broadway as they glided high above New York City. The three friends swooped down from the night sky toward the lights that lit up the streets almost as bright as day. After sleeping on a Scottish castle for one thousand years, the Gargoyles were fascinated by the strange and modern world of New York City. The more they explored it, the more they found new and wonderful things—like these twinkling, flashing, arcing lights.

Lexington landed lightly above a huge sign advertising photo film. As he watched it, the sign showed a camera that gave a sudden bright flash. He blinked and then looked at the back of the sign. Wires ran from its back to some boxes nearby on the rooftop. "Magic ropes," Lexington said. "Humans use many of these." Then he noticed another, more interesting rooftop display and glided to it. This one had a sign, too, with a large ball high above it. Although both the sign and the ball were covered with rows of lightbulbs, they were dark. "Must be broken," Lexington said. "Maybe I can fix 'em."

Broadway, meanwhile, was closer to the ground. The smell of hotdogs from a cart was too good to pass up. He needed a snack to get him through to his next mealtime...which usually came right after his snack. "These smell great!" he called to the vendor.

"Buck fifty, mac," the vendor said. Then he looked up. "T-t-take all you want!" the vendor yelled as he ran away.

"I only want five!" Broadway called as he helped himself.

Brooklyn was watching another vendor. In front of a sign that said "Only two more days!" was a table that held glittering gold and silver hats. "Get yer hats now!" the vendor called. "Don't wait till the last minute!" Puzzled, Brooklyn watched to see if anyone stopped for the hats. Humans did many unusual things, he had learned. Just four nights ago, he had seen them lighting up trees in their houses. Elisa Maza, their human friend, had said they were celebrating something called "Christmas." And now, apparently, some other human celebration was coming up.

"I like this place!" Broadway whispered as he joined Brooklyn. "Lots of good food."

"And amazing machines," added Lexington as he landed beside them. "I want to come back here."

Brooklyn nodded. "Me, too. I think something important is going to happen here soon. Let's go tell Goliath."

Goliath, their leader, was waiting for them at their clock tower home. Elisa, who worked for the police, was with him, too. As the trio excitedly described the new place they had discovered, even Hudson, the elder Gargoyle, and Bronx, the Gargoyles' dog, came to listen.

"Sounds like you found Times Square," Elisa told them.

"Yes, there were calendars and clocks everywhere," said Lexington.

Elisa smiled but she didn't look very happy. "I have to work there in two nights. Sort of a birthday tradition for me," she said.

"What's a birthday?" Broadway asked.

But Elisa's answer had to wait. It was getting close to dawn. The Gargoyles took their places on the rooftop, and as the sun rose, their flesh turned to stone for the daylight hours.

The next night, Goliath explained what Elisa meant about birthdays. "Each year, humans celebrate the day they were born," he told the others. When they looked puzzled, he added,

"Being born is like hatching. But for some reason, Elisa must work while the others celebrate. She thinks December thirty-first is a bad day for her birthday."

"That's it!" said Brooklyn. "That's what the signs meant, Goliath, they're going to celebrate Elisa's birthday in Times Square!"

Goliath looked doubtful, but Lexington added. "It's true! Everyone was talking about her new year!"

"We could throw her a party there so she can have at least a little fun while she works," Brooklyn said. "I'll get the hats!"

"I'll bring the food," said Broadway.

At the mention of food, Bronx growled happily. "Nay, boy," said Hudson, patting the dog's head. "You and I will stay here and guard our home."

Goliath frowned. "Perhaps we should all do that. I don't want you attracting attention or causing any trouble for Elisa."

"No problem, Goliath," said Brooklyn. "It'll be a rooftop party."

"And I've got the perfect rooftop," Lexington added. "It's all set up for a party, with a platform and a big fancy ball and lights. They aren't working now, but I'll fix them!"

"Well, all right," said Goliath. "I suppose you want this to be a surprise," he added, smiling as they nodded eagerly. "Very well, then, I'll see to it that Elisa gets to her birthday party."

Brooklyn, Broadway, and Lexington were surprised to see a crowd as they circled Times

Square. "Elisa sure has a lot of friends," Broadway said. "I should have brought more food."

"Well, at least some of them have their own hats," said Brooklyn.

"Look!" Lexington said. "There are people on our roof!"

"There are people on all the roofs," Brooklyn added. "I have a feeling Goliath isn't going to like this."

Goliath wasn't liking it. As he swooped above the crowd searching for Elisa, it became harder and harder to stay out of sight. He glanced at the rooftop where the others were waiting and saw some humans running away from his friends. With a soft angry growl, he headed for the rooftop.

Meanwhile, Elisa was taking a break in a patrol car, trying to keep her teeth from chattering. It was always freezing on her birthday. "Just once," she muttered, "I'd like to celebrate like everyone else." People at the station had been nice enough, but not even her birthday could get her out of Times Square duty on New Year's Eve. Everybody available had to work it.

She was just stepping out of the car when two men raced up to her.

"Up on the roof!" one gasped. "Big bats! Huge wings! Fangs!"

"And one of them said, 'Hi, guys!'" the other added.

Oh no! It had to be the Gargoyles.

"We couldn't get the clock hooked up," the other worker said. "If people miss the countdown to midnight, they'll riot!"

"I'll handle it," Elisa said. "And don't be telling anyone else about this. We don't want a panic."

Elisa fumed as she punched the elevator button. She knew it wasn't the Gargoyles' fault. They didn't know about New Year's Eve. But they did know they were supposed to stay out of sight.

As she opened the door to the roof Elisa saw Lexington and the others near the sign. "What are you doing?" she yelled.

"Elisa!" Brooklyn said. "Where's Goliath?"

"I'm right here," said a deep voice behind them. "And we're all leaving now. I told you to keep out of sight."

"He's right!" Elisa snapped. "What were you thinking? It's New Year's Eve!"

"It's your birthday, Elisa," said Lexington. "We just wanted to surprise you."

"We got hats," Brooklyn said, holding one out to her.

"And food," Broadway said, handing her the only hotdog he had managed not to eat.

For a minute—a very short minute—Elisa thought she might cry. Then she caught herself and said, "We still have to get off this roof. It's five minutes to midnight. They've got to get this fixed so—"

"Don't worry, Elisa, I fixed it," Lexington said.

"Come on." Goliath picked up Elisa, and the others followed him to another rooftop.

As they landed, Elisa looked back. Sure enough, the clock had started its midnight countdown. They could hear the crowd chanting, "Ten...nine...eight...." But well before "one," the counting was drowned out by cheers and noisemakers. The Gargoyles also cheered as the ball, bright with lights now, dropped toward the clock to bring in the new year.

Elisa looked back at the clock again. But where she—and the crowd—expected to see "1996!" flashing, there was an entirely different message:

"Happy Birthday, Elisa!"

"SEEING" AIR

Air is constantly moving. You can feel it, but you can't see it. Air is invisible. However, a special kind of photography captures the movement of air on film. That's the secret of the picture above. It shows air flowing past a model of an aircraft.

Light rays usually travel in a straight line. But disturbances in the air cause rays of light to bend.

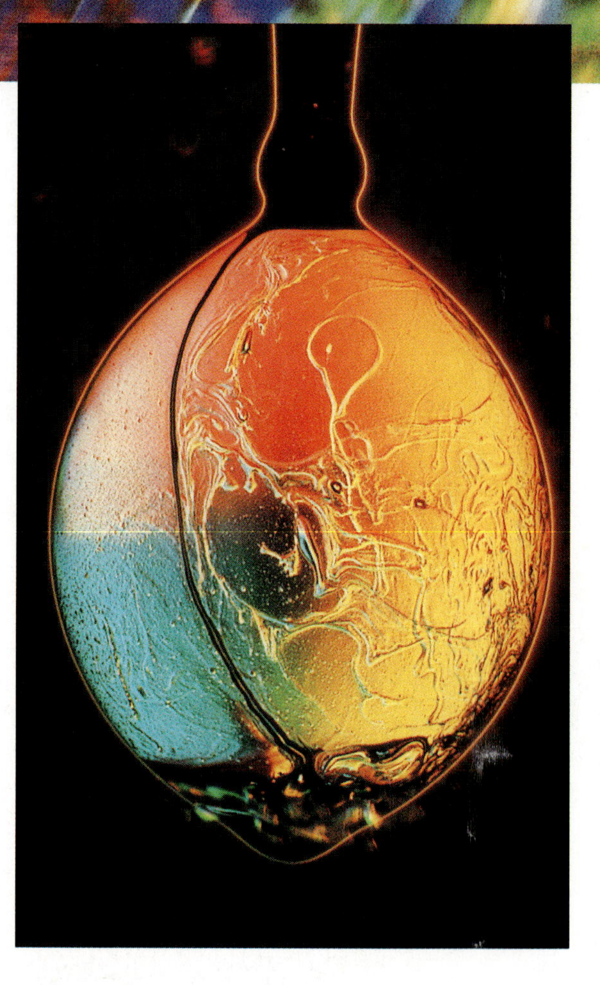

Light rays bend as they pass through a soap bubble and appear as glowing colors.

For example, air is disturbed when it flows around an object in its path. As light rays pass through this air disturbance, they bend. Light rays also bend when they pass from cool air to warm air.

These photos were made using a regular camera and some special equipment. The subjects were placed in front of a curved mirror. Most of the light rays bounced straight back from the mirror toward the camera. But rays that were bent bounced back toward the camera in a scattered pattern. A special filter was used to add colors to the different types of rays. In this way, the images of the bent light rays were recorded on film—and, like magic, air became visible!

Left: This special photo shows how warm air rises from a steaming cup of cocoa. Right: This regular photo shows the setup that was used to take that picture.

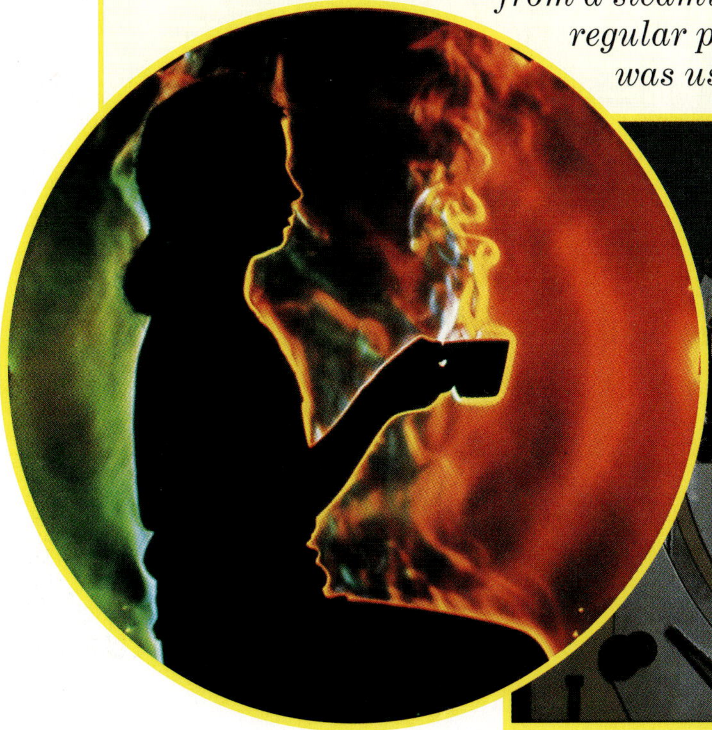

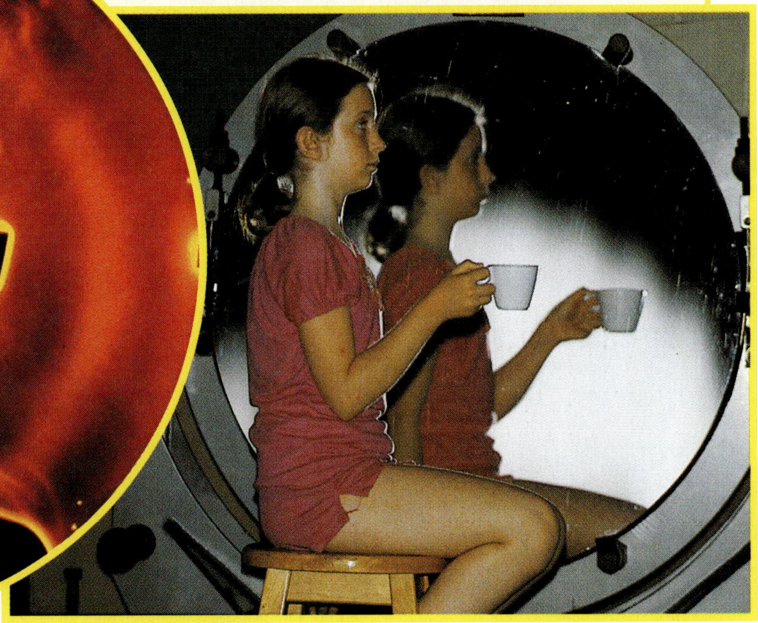

BODY ACTIONS

Your body is smart! It always knows what's going on around you—and it reacts in its own special way.

For example, if you are embarrassed your face reacts by **blushing**. How does this happen? When you feel uncomfortable, your brain tells your heart to pump faster. It also tells the tiny blood vessels, or capillaries, in your body to get wider, so they can carry the extra blood being pumped by the heart. You have more capillaries in the skin of your face than anywhere else on your body. So everyone can see the rushing blood turn your face a bright pink.

Do you ever get **butterflies in your stomach**? That's one way your body tells you that you are very nervous. And when you are nervous, your body's adrenal glands release a special chemical into your bloodstream. That chemical makes your stomach tense up and produce more acid. And this is what makes you feel as if a bunch of butterflies were doing flip flops inside you.

Have you ever been really cold? Or frightened? If your answer is yes, you have probably had **goose bumps**. Your skin is covered with tiny hairs. At the base of each hair is a tiny muscle. When you are cold or frightened, these muscles tighten. This makes the hairs stand up, which causes the skin around the hairs to form "goose bumps."

Do your hands and feet look like wrinkled prunes when you get out of a long bath? **Shriveled skin** happens because the oil made by glands in your skin gets washed away. When this occurs, the water in your skin oozes out—and your hands and feet wrinkle. This doesn't happen to other parts of your body because they have more oil than your hands and feet.

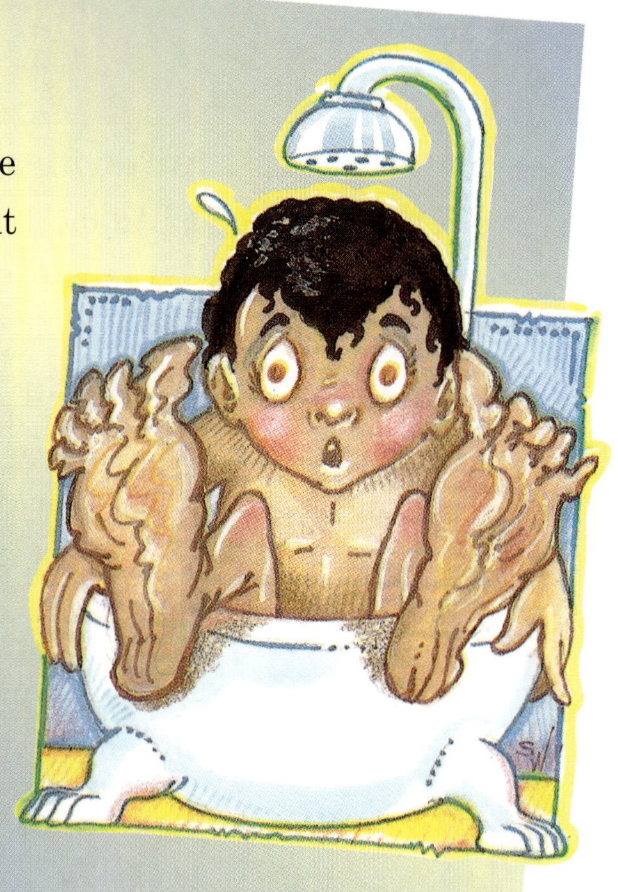

When you wake up, do you have **sand in your eyes**? This occurs because your tears contain salt and other chemicals. Tears are constantly given off by glands behind your eyelids. When you sleep, tears that collect at the edges of your eyelids dry out. Only the chemicals remain. They form the crusty, sticky "sand" that you rub from your eyes in the morning.

If someone takes your picture using a flash, you may see **spots in front of your eyes** for a few seconds. Why? When light enters your eyes, it hits the cells in the retina (the thin inner coat of the eyeball). The light causes chemical changes in these cells. These chemical changes cause messages to be sent to the brain about what you are seeing. But if you look at a very bright light, such as a camera flash, the cells are exposed to too much light. The overexposed cells react by creating the spots in front of your eyes.

Why Do We Yawn?

When you are tired or bored, your body becomes less alert. Your heartbeat and breathing slow down, so there's less oxygen in your bloodstream. Your brain reacts by forcing a yawn, which allows more oxygen to enter the blood. But scientists can't explain why yawning is catching—why you sometimes yawn just because someone nearby has yawned. Even reading about a yawn can make you yawn. Are you yawning now?

THE JOKES ON YOU!

Why does the kangaroo think that 1996 is a great year?

Because it likes leap years the best!

What's full of holes but still holds water?

A sponge!

Why do hummingbirds hum?

They don't know how to yodel!

What did the big firecracker say to the little firecracker?

My pop is bigger than your pop!

What comes once in a minute, twice in a moment, and never in a hundred years?

The letter M!

Why did the electric eel get a punk haircut?

He wanted to shock his parents!